I ♥ W16

AGENT WEASEL

WEASEL

AND T...   ...OY GANG

HODDER

HODDER CHILDREN'S BOOKS

First published in Great Britain in 2018 by Hodder and Stoughton

1 3 5 7 9 10 8 6 4 2

Text and illustrations copyright © Nick East, 2019

ISBN 978 1 444 94527 0

Printed and bound in Great Britain by Clays Ltd, Elcograph S.p.A.
The paper and board used in this book are made from wood from
responsible sources

Hodder Children's Books
An imprint of Hachette Children's Group
Part of Hodder and Stoughton
Carmelite House
50 Victoria Embankment
London EC4Y 0DZ
An Hachette UK Company
www.hachette.co.uk
www.hachettechildrens.co.uk

FOR LOU, SO TRULY KIND AND LOVELY.
BUT WHO ALWAYS GETS THE BOARD GAMES
OUT AT CHRISTMAS ...
ARRRRGH!

In a forgotten corner of the countryside
lies a small green wood, much like any other.
But take a closer look and it is far from ordinary.
For this is the United Woodlands – home of
Agent Weasel, legendary super-spy. A place full
of adventure, mystery – and an incredibly
wide variety of edible nuts.

CHAPTER 1

It was a crisp autumn morning deep in the heart of the United Woodlands. Things were all go at top-secret Flaky-Bark Cottage. Agent Weasel – renowned WI6 super-spy – had a few days off from the usual spy stuff. But instead of chilling out with his feet up, he was busying away on a particularly tricky and dangerous operation.

Perched at the top of a rickety old stepladder, Weasel was building a rather magnificent card tower. An unusual task for a top-notch spy, you might think. But for training purposes this was an excellent test of courage, skill and complete daftness!

As Weasel reached over to place the final card and beat his all-time record, the extremely loud spy hotline rang.

WOBBLE

DRING
DRING
DRING

DRRRRINGG-DRRRRINGG!

His legs began to tremble.

DRRRRINGG-DRRRRINGG!

The stepladder began to wobble.

DRRRRINGG-DRRRRINGG!

With a *GULP*, Weasel realised this wasn't going to end well. And ... *WHOOSH, BANG, CRASH!* Down he came like a ... erm ... stack of cards.

With a pitiful groan, he tried to get up, but he could not move a whisker. Weasel was now somehow knitted between the rungs of the old wooden stepladder. *How by all that's SQUISHY AND BRAMBLY did that happen?* he wondered.

DRRRRRINGG—DRRRRRINGG! the phone continued.

There was an abrupt *knock-knock-knock*

at the front door. 'Weasel, are you in there?' squeaked a familiar voice.

Now who could that be? Weasel could not think straight. He must have clobbered his noggin harder than he'd thought. Stars spun around his head and his eyes were seriously crossed!

DRRRRINGG—DRRRRINGG!

'Weasel, it's Doorkins,' went on the voice from outside. 'I was in the garden tending to my prize pumpkin when I heard a dreadful crash. Are you all right?'

'Hmmmmmm … Doorkins … ?' Weasel said, still rather dazed.

The voice now squeaked more urgently. 'If you do not answer me, Weasel, I will have no choice but to bash this door in!'

'AH, DOORKINS!' Weasel remembered.

How could he possibly forget his faithful dormouse pal and co-adventurer, who'd lived in the tree above Flaky-Bark Cottage since they were little pinkie newborns?

This chap was one talented mouse: writer for the *Daily Conker* newspaper; expert tree-climber-upper; green-pawed champion pumpkin-grower. And being a dormouse, Doorkins was as cute as a button, too. Weasel was proud to call him a friend.

DRRRRINGG—DRRRRINGG!

There was a cry from outside and a pitter-patter of tiny galloping paws. 'RIGHT-O, HERE I COME!'

BANG ...

'OUCH!'

And the hefty door swung open.

'Ah – already unlocked!' croaked Doorkins

as he rubbed a bump on top of his cute, furry head. Wiping his paws on the welcome mat, he staggered in.

DRRRRINGG—DRRRRINGG!

'Good morning, old chum,' Weasel said, still in a tangled heap on the living-room floor. 'How's that amazing pumpkin doing? Hope she'll be ripe and ready for the Autumn Big Bash tomorrow afternoon.'

'This one will definitely be my best ever!' Doorkins told him. 'The Autumn Big Bash won't know what's hit it!'

DRRRRINGG—DRRRRINGG!

The Autumn Big Bash was the fair of all fairs in the United Woodlands. And Doorkins's magnificent pumpkins had won the coveted Best in Show Acorn Cup four seasons in a row.

DRRRRINGG—DRRRRINGG! went the phone – AGAIN!

'Be a good fellow and get that for me, would you?' asked Weasel politely. 'I'm a bit, er … tied up at the moment!'

Doorkins picked up the annoyingly loud ringy thing and handed it over. Weasel fumbled the phone, still dizzy from his unfortunate stepladder kerfuffle.

'Ahem! Hello Weasel, Agent Weasel,' he announced.

CHAPTER 2

Weasel pressed the phone against his ear with a confused, squinty sort of expression on his face.

'I can't hear a thing. I tell you, Doorkins, this phone is more like a lukewarm line than a hotline if you ask me.'

Doorkins patiently took the phone and turned it the right way up, then handed it back

FLIP

to the rather red-faced super-spy.

'Agent Weasel, are you there?' an irritated voice said at the other end. It was H, head-honcho hedgehog at Woodland Intelligence (WI6 to you and me).

'Yes, I'm here, H. Just a slight technical hitch, but all fine now,' Weasel said, with a quick sideways glance at Doorkins.

'Good, good, good!' H replied. 'Stinky goings-on out there in civilian woodland, Weasel. I'm afraid … we're going to need you on this one,' she mumbled half-heartedly. 'Reports have been literally flying into Hedgequarters over the past few hours. Usually by chaffinch, and you know what that lot are like for gossip!'

Agent Weasel had heard about these shocking deeds on the Woodland News

Bulletin that very morning. Rabbit warrens had been peppered with itching powder. Vole holes purposely caved-in. A whole family of sleeping badgers had had their bottoms shaved. And these were only a few of the many wrongdoings. It was complete mayhem!

EEEK!

BARE BADGER BOTTOMS!

'Principal Pine Marten, our distinguished leader, wants this situation dealt with – and dealt with fast!' said H. 'And the thing is, all my top agents – I mean, *other* agents – are out in the field. Farmer Garrett's muddy field, that is – dealing with the fiddly Humongous Hole in the Hedge case and the Tricky Cowpat Plop plot. So ... I only have one agent to turn to. And that's you, Agent Weasel!'

She sighed. It wasn't that Weasel didn't get the job done. He always caught his animal. But he seemed unable to do things by the book.

VOTE
PINE MARTEN

And at WI6, doing things by the book was of the utmost importance.

'We suspect a gang led by a criminal mastermind!' H continued. 'Could be the FFG?'

The FFG stood for the Fiendish Fox Gang. These guys were proper baddies, doing wicked stuff just for the fun of it and then some. They were giving foxes a very bad name indeed. And in Weasel's opinion, this had the FFG's big, sticky paw prints all over it. He pondered, twizzling his whiskers: *Find their despicable den, stake 'em out and see if we can catch these crooks in the act!*

'You can count on me, ma'am!' said Agent Weasel proudly.

'Well I-I-I do hope so,' stumbled H. 'And … Weasel?'

'Yes, H?'

'No … you know … *hiccups!*' And with that she hung up.

How rude! Hiccups, what did she mean, hiccups? he thought, wriggling around in an attempt to free himself from the pesky stepladder.

'Doorkins, my friend! It's time to break out the stakeout kit. This just got real!' Weasel announced dramatically.

'And maybe also a saw to get you out of this, er … hiccup?' suggested Doorkins, waving a paw at Weasel's unfortunate situation.

HUMPH! thought Weasel, crossing his arms and responding with a grouchy nod.

CHAPTER 3

'Ahhh!' sighed a relaxed Agent Weasel. 'I do love a good stakeout, Doorkins.' He was munching away on a delicious egg and cress sandwich and sipping from a mug of the chocolatiest hot chocolate ever.

Being on a stakeout generally involves

secretly peeking at someone from a safe and cosy hiding place. But also it absolutely must involve a scrummy picnic and tasty hot drink to keep you going – at least it must according to Agent Weasel!

'Very important to be comfortable on a stakeout – don't you think, Doorkins?' said Weasel. Doorkins nodded enthusiastically, his cheeks stuffed full of dandelion fairy cakes.

The friends were snugly tucked up inside the WI6 portable tree-stump hide. They'd placed it near a rotten oak tree, in a particularly dodgy part of the United Woodlands called Dingy Dell.

Owl Force 1 – crack flying squadron and all round feathery good guys – had reported suspicious goings-on in a recent fly-by of the area. It was the best lead they had.

DINGY
DELL

Weasel squinted
through the viewfinder
of the WI6 Welliescope
mounted to the top of the hide.
This was a very special and complicated piece
of WI6 spy kit. It consisted of a periscope with
a stinky old welly stuck on top for camouflage,
so they could see out of the top of the hide
without being seen. The stinkier and more
battered the welly, the better!

Surrounding the rotten oak tree, Agent Weasel could see a ramshackle log wall, topped with prickly bramble thorns. A rickety wooden gate was painted with shoddy red lettering that stated:

Or else what? thought Weasel. *Or else we'll invite you in for tea and cakes and a fun game of hide and seek? Or else you can come say hello to my granny and have a look at my excellent acorn collection?* Who knew? It was not at all clear.

One thing was for sure. It looked very much like the kind of place a bunch of naughty scheming foxes might hang out!

VRUMM—VRUMM! Was that the distant sound of an engine? Weasel's spy super-senses began to tingle. Something heavy was trundling through the woods, and it seemed to be coming straight towards them!

CHAPTER 4

As Doorkins chomped away in a hurry – trying hard to swallow a mouthful of dandelion fairy cake – Agent Weasel watched a huge grey truck arrive at the gate. It was pretty hard not to notice the tall, solid yellow letters on the side reading: 'FFG'.

Hmmmm! Very low-key, thought Weasel, raising his eyebrows in surprise.

A shifty-looking fox jumped down from the truck's cab. She pulled out a clipboard, made a few scribbles, then prowled around to the back of the truck.

With a loud *CLANG* and *SQUEEEEAK*, the back doors flew open and two rather bulky foxes tumbled on to the woodland floor.

YEEOW

CLANK

They moaned and grumbled as they dusted themselves off.

'Well, thanks a bunch, Ginger!' one of the big foxes muttered under his breath to the fox with the clipboard.

'GINGER?' she growled back. 'It's BOSS to you, you BIG CLODHOPPER, and don't you forget it!'

As the two big foxes nervously stood to attention, Weasel got a better look at them. Twins, he thought – they looked almost exactly the same, apart from the permanent scowl on one, like there was a bad smell under his nose. And on the front of their poorly knitted jumpers – the kind a well-meaning granny might give you for Christmas – were the names 'VIV' and 'VIC'.

As soon as Ginger looked down at her

clipboard again, the twins began to bicker.

'That's the last time I go in the back with you, Viv. I'm sure you've given me fleas – again!' whinged Vic, frantically scratching under his chin.

'Well, at least I don't smell of mouldy blue cheese, do I? You should try having a bath every now and again!' said Viv, pinching the end of her twitching snout.

As they fussed around arguing, a large, rusty drum slowly rolled out from the back of the truck. *BOFF!* it went as it hit the ground in a shower of fallen leaves.

Viv and Vic panicked, diving for cover …

But the drum rocked to a standstill.

'YOU COMPLETE CONKERS!' barked Ginger as she stalked over, waving her clipboard. 'Lying around here won't get anything done. Get that drum through the gate – AT ONCE! Let's not keep the BIG BOSS waiting or we'll be in some serious DOO-DOO and no mistake!'

Hmmmm, BIG BOSS, pondered Weasel. *Could this be the mysterious leader of the Fiendish Fox Gang? Were this lot the cause of all the recent mischief?* He and Doorkins were going to need more evidence, and quick!

The twins sheepishly set the drum upright with great care. There was something particularly odd about this, thought Weasel. Turning the dial on the Welliescope, he zoomed in for a better view. And there, stencilled on the side of the drum in bright red paint, grinned an evil-looking skull with the words: '*DANGER! ITCHING POWDER!*'

'HA HAA! WE'VE GOT 'EM!' exclaimed

Weasel – at the exact same moment as Doorkins was pouring himself a nice big mug of steaming, chocolatey hot chocolate.

Doorkins jolted in shock, spilling the drink over his surprised chum.

'AAAARRRGGGHHH – PRICKLY BUM THISTLES!' screeched Weasel, as the boiling liquid sloshed down the front of his best WI6 polo-neck spy jumper.

Thinking quickly, Doorkins stuffed a half

finished egg and cress sandwich into the super-spy's chops, because silence on a WI6 stakeout was of the utmost importance.

With Weasel quiet for the moment, Doorkins peeked through the Welliescope viewfinder. He jumped back in shock. Three fierce foxes were creeping towards the WI6 tree-stump hide. And the big grumpy one had pulled out a splurge gun, the FFG's dreaded weapon of choice!

CHAPTER 5

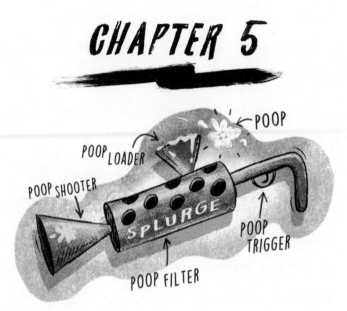

POOP

POOP LOADER

POOP SHOOTER

SPLURGE

POOP TRIGGER

POOP FILTER

'Oh, blithering bog-moss! Not another WI6 spy jumper down the plughole!' spluttered Weasel, swallowing the half finished sarnie.

Poor Weasel felt a little sorry for himself. He seemed to have seriously bad luck with jumpers – he could get through six to eight of them a week, and that was just relaxing at home. At work his record was twenty-one! Maybe a waterproof spy mac would be more practical. But Weasel did love a smartly knitted jumper. 'Another one for the dry cleaners, Doorkins!'

But Doorkins did not reply. Wide-eyed, he pointed a shaky paw at the Welliescope.

Drums full of itching powder were pretty scary, thought Weasel – but not that scary. He shifted over to take a look.

With a yelp and a high-pitched bottom squeak, Weasel spun to face the frozen dormouse. 'The foxes are coming this way!'

Doorkins nodded frantically.

'And they have a s-s-splurge gun!'

As a WI6 agent, Weasel knew only too well the awesome power of these nasty weapons.

GRRRRRR

If a flock of pigeons has ever plopped on you all at once, then you'll know what it's like to be hit by a fearsome splurge gun.

The pair began to panic.

Now an ordinary-looking tree stump or a perfectly innocent wellie wouldn't normally get a second glance, even from a wily bunch of foxes. But it was not normal stump behaviour to jiggle around like a grooving badger, making strange *trumpy-squeak-squeak* noises.

The foxes skulked forward for a closer look.

'Don't panic, don't panic … !' Doorkins muttered in shock.

WHOOOSH

Weasel needed a plan, but he couldn't think straight with Doorkins in such a state. Picking up a glass of lemonade, Weasel threw the contents in his friend's face. Doorkins spat and spluttered, regaining his senses.

'Sorry, old chum!' Weasel apologised.

'Ah! Absolutely,' Doorkins said, wiping the fizzy pop from his face.

The foxes were almost upon them.

Weasel mumbled away, racking his brains for a solution. 'Hmmm … no, no, not that, Aunty wouldn't like it. Hmmm … no, too fussy by far. Er … no, much too sticky. AHA! I HAVE IT, DOORKINS! RUUUUUUUUUUUUUUUN!'

Talk about putting a plan straight into action. Up popped the stump, revealing two pairs of furry legs and a half eaten picnic, then it belted off into the woods at top speed.

The foxes stood rooted to the spot, jaws gaping. It took them a few moments to realise what was going on.

'SPIES! AFTER THEM!' howled Ginger.

CHAPTER 6

The four-legged tree stump began to weave in and out of the trees, picking up speed as it went. The poor foxes were struggling to keep up!

'OOOH, I think I'm going to be sick!' moaned Vic. 'Wish I hadn't had that massive plate of snails and chips for breakfast!'

'Stop w-whinging, bog breath!' gasped

Ginger. She tripped on a gnarly old tree root and went flying snout first into a pile of dead leaves. *AAAAAARGH–SWOOOSH–THUNK!*

Viv and Vic skidded to a stop.

Trying to contain a snigger, Viv peeked around the tree to see if Ginger was OK.

'K-keep after them, you pea brains … YUCK!' Ginger spluttered, spitting out a mouthful of mouldy plants and pointing at the fleeing spies.

'YES, BOSS!' they barked.

Our intrepid friends were bombing along quite nicely. Doorkins clung to Weasel's back, peering through the Welliescope and shouting 'LEFT!' or 'RIGHT!'

TEE–HEE

COUGH

each time they approached an obstacle.

Dormice are known for their speed over a short distance – particularly up trees. But there was no way Doorkins could keep up with Weasel over such a long stretch, so he was clinging on to his friend's back as tight as he could, hoping for the best.

As for Agent Weasel, he came from a long line of champion woodland runners.

His Great-Uncle Bertrand Weasel had won the Woodland Mile Classic eight times in a row. Unfortunately, on his ninth attempt, Bertrand had been suffering from a serious bout of squeaky-bottom syndrome. He gave off such tremendous windy pops that he gassed half his opponents and a number of spectators to boot.

Fortunately, Weasel did not suffer from the same trumpy issues – which was good news for Doorkins, as no emergency gas masks were provided in the WI6 tree-stump hide.

CRUUUNCH!

'Sniffling sneezewort, what was that?' exclaimed Weasel, as a terrible shudder rocked through them.

'OH, PLOP!' said Doorkins. The Welliescope must have hit a low branch and broken off. Doorkins peered into the viewfinder – yep, everything had gone black!

'Right or left, Doorkins, *right or left?*' insisted Weasel, powering along at incredible speed and completely unaware of the new danger.

'I think we have a teeny-weeny problem, Weasel,' admitted Doorkins.

Agent Weasel quickly put two and two together. 'We're running blind, aren't we, Doorkins? Now, let's not panic.' Weasel glanced over his shoulder at the dormouse, whose eyes were wide with alarm.

'AAAAAAAAAAAAAAARRGGHH!' they both screeched, in complete and utter panic.

CHAPTER 7

The furry-legged tree stump seemed to have lost all sense of direction. It swerved around all over the place, then, without warning, zipped off to the left and out of sight. The fox twins screeched to a halt.

'OH!' said Vic in disbelief.

A misty woodland clearing lay ahead of the foxes … but not just any misty woodland clearing, one that was completely full of tree stumps. Hundreds of tree stumps!

'What do we do now?' moaned Vic. He flopped back against a bendy tree, which struggled to support his massive weight.

'Let's just pretend they gave us the slip,' suggested Viv. 'What trouble can a couple of little spies cause us?'

'We can't do that!' bawled Vic. 'If Ginger or the Big Boss found out, we'd be for it. The last fox who behaved kindly had all his tail fur plucked out as punishment. One hair at a time!'

The twins shuddered at the thought. They would have to search the clearing.

But just as they were about to get underway, Ginger burst in.

'S-STOP!' she panted, her big pink tongue lolling out. 'C-could be a t-trap!' she wheezed, holding a paw up to show she was catching her breath.

Viv gave a little giggle.

'I have a b-better idea,' Ginger said. 'Send in the SNIFFER ANTS!'

'AWWW, boss, but the sniffer ants are all the way back at the truck!' moaned Vic, still leaning on the bendy tree.

Ginger narrowed her eyes in an especially scary way. 'Well, as you are so bothered about it,' she said to Vic, rather too calmly, 'YOU'D BETTER GET MOVING AND MAKE IT QUICK, YOU BIG LUMP!'

Vic cringed at the ear-bashing.

Viv couldn't help let out another little titter.

'AND AS FOR YOU … !' Ginger screeched, pointing a threatening paw at Viv.

Vic dragged himself up, muttering under his breath,

THWACK

and the tree he had been leaning on snapped back, whacking Ginger on top of the head. Down she went in the manky leaves with a big *SQUELCH!*

Viv desperately tried not to hoot with laughter as Vic sloped back to Dingy Dell, glancing over his shoulder as he went.

Meanwhile, in the tree-stump hide, Weasel and Doorkins could hear a commotion somewhere nearby. They assumed it was probably the foxes, but with the muffling mist and the hide's special WI6 soundproofing, it was tricky to hear anything.

Even with Doorkins's super-duper dormouse hearing, it felt a bit like having a thick woolly sock over your head. Which he had in fact taken to doing recently, when the WI6 Spy Choir were practising at Weasel's cottage. Doorkins would never tell his best pal this, but they sounded like a gaggle of geese being hauled through a prickly hedge backwards. But singing (if you wanted to call it that) made Weasel happy. So on Wednesday evenings Doorkins would find a good book, pull a sock over his ears and sit tight – it was no biggie!

As Doorkins and Weasel waited in the tree-stump hide, Ginger was scraping the mud and leaves off her jacket while Viv scanned the clearing with keen eyes. All seemed quiet.

The silence was broken by Vic's lumbering return. He staggered along, huffing and puffing, straining to hold a tall, narrow packing case with the words 'HANDLE WITH CARE' stamped on the side.

'Ah, at last – the wanderer returns!' mocked

Ginger, stepping up to inspect the case just as it began to slip through Vic's paws.

THWUUMP! it went, straight on to Ginger's toes.

'YEEEEEEEEEEOOW!' she yelped, hopping around like a demented frog. 'Can't you read? HANDLE WITH CARE, it says! Right, I've had enough of you – you know what's coming!' And she jabbed a paw into Vic's chest.

'No, not that, boss, anything but that!' pleaded Vic.

'Yes, I'm going to hit you where it really hurts! NO PUDDING FOR YOU TONIGHT!'

'NOOOOOOOOOOOOOOO!' howled Vic.

HANDLE WITH CARE

TRAMP TRAMP TRAMP

'Now get those ants released and NO MORE LIP!'

'Just *mean*!' sniffed the big fox.

Vic knelt and slid up a tiny hatch at the front of the case. Almost immediately, a line of very small, shiny black ants marched out one by one and headed off into the misty clearing.

Ginger rubbed her paws together. These were no ordinary ants. They were experts, trained for one thing and one thing only. To sniff out pesky SPIES!

CHAPTER 8

The ants were leading the three foxes in a merry old dance. They trailed through a bank of extremely prickly bramble bushes, a large clump of nasty stinging nettles, a big, dank patch of squelchy mud … and now, to top it all, they were crawling into an abandoned badger sett with a distinctly whiffy smell!

Ginger was fuming. She limped on her injured paw and there was a nice lump forming on top of her head. But worst of all, the ants' tracking senses were all out of sorts.

'If only that big mud-snuffler hadn't

dropped the case!' she grumbled under her breath.

Without warning, the ants came to an abrupt stop. They turned with military precision and trudged back out of the badger sett.

Had they actually detected something at last?

'This looks more promising,' said Ginger. 'Maybe now we're on the right track!'

Meanwhile, back in the WI6 tree-stump hide, Weasel and Doorkins pondered what game they should play to pass the time. Weasel thought it might help take his friend's mind off the rather nerve-racking situation, and Weasel did love a game. At Christmas he was the one – and there's always one! – who would bellow out: 'GAME TIME, EVERYBODY!' just as you were about to take a nice nap after stuffing yourself stupid with Christmas pudding.

'What about I Spy, old chum?' Weasel whispered excitedly.

Now, Doorkins was not much of a game fan. He would prefer to be snug in his favourite comfy chair, with a good gardening book and a nice cup of tea. And really, I Spy? How was *that* going to work inside the WI6 tree-stump hide? Well, it looked like he was about to find out!

'Come on, Doorkins, why so glum? You go first,' said Weasel.

'Ahhhhhh,' sighed Doorkins. 'I spy with my little eye ... something beginning with A.'

There wasn't a great deal to see apart from a patch of yellowy-green moss and a few mouldy leaves. Definitely no apples, or acorns, or ...

'*YEEE-OUCH!*' Weasel yelped, feeling

a painful nip on his bottom. He sprang up,
bashing his head on the hide's ceiling.

THUUNK!

'YEEOOOW!' yelled Doorkins, as he did
the same. *THUUNK!* went his head.

'ANTS, Weasel!' cried Doorkins, pointing
to a small knothole. 'A is for ANTS!'

Sure enough, a column of small, shiny black ants were trooping in through the knothole. And oh yes, they had begun to bite, like the maddest bitey things that had ever bitten!

'OOOO, EEEK, OUCH, AAAARGH!' Weasel and Doorkins bounced around like brown hares at a trampoline party. They had to make a choice: get nibbled silly, or run for it.

'BETTER MAKE A MOVE!' yelled Weasel. And off they scarpered. But something was not quite right. Weasel looked down to see his legs motoring ten to the dozen, but they didn't actually seem to be going anywhere! It felt like someone or something had a hold of them …

The next second they were pulled out of the hide by the scruff of the neck. Squinting in the daylight, they were now eye to eye with a huge and rather angry-looking fox!

'You beetle-munchers cost me pudding tonight!' snarled Vic, as Weasel and Doorkins dangled from his big, meaty paws.

'Leave off, Vic – I think they're kind of cute,' said Viv, peeping over his shoulder.

'SHUT IT, YOU TWO!' growled Ginger. 'Get these spy scum in the bag. Von Fluff will deal with them now!'

VON FLUFF! Could this be the FFG's menacing leader? thought Weasel.

But there really was no way around it. They would have to go along with these hooligans if they wanted to confront this von Fluff character in person.

Just as Weasel was considering some charming banter to get the foxes on his side, everything went black!

CHAPTER 9

Our two daring heroes had been stuffed into a seriously scratchy old sack. The sack was slung over the big, bad-tempered fox's shoulder, and every time he took a step there was a strong waft of mouldy cheese. With that and the helpless bumping and rolling around, our pair began to feel very queasy indeed!

'D-don't worry, old pal, I know exactly w-where we are!' muttered Weasel, bouncing upside down with his bottom end stuck in Doorkins's face. 'I know these woods like the b-back of my paw. I will plot our path by s-smell, sound and taste alone! Every crunchy leaf, every tweeting bird, every b-breath of wind will guide me. My s-spy super-senses will never let us d—!'

'WE'RE AT THE HIDEOUT, BOSS,' boomed Viv. 'HAVE YOU GOT THE KEY FOR THE GATE?'

'Ah. Oh well, better think of something else clever and spy-like,' said Weasel. He closed his eyes for a moment, feeling suddenly not all that clever and spy-like at all. Doorkins gave him a comforting pat on the back.

CLUNK, CLANG, SQUEEEAKK! The

gate opened and the fox gang marched through.

Weasel began to frantically rummage around in his WI6-issue spy jumper. Doorkins couldn't understand why. Perhaps Weasel had picked up some fleas from the itchy sack?

'Aha!' Weasel whispered.

And pulled out a rather large and overripe banana.

'No, not that!'

Weasel rummaged around again, and this time plucked out a small wooden box with a series of air holes drilled in the top.

'Yesss!' said Weasel, as he carefully wiggled the lid off. To Doorkins's delight, a pretty little moth fluttered out, landing on Weasel's shoulder.

'Well, I never!' the dormouse said.

'This is Muriel – she's my personally trained, elite homing moth.' Weasel beamed with pride. 'Get word back to Hedgequarters, my pocket-sized beauty!' he whispered in her tiny moth ear.

Muriel had saved Weasel's bacon on a number of occasions. Paws crossed she could do the same again!

Suddenly they were dropped to the ground. *OOOOF!*

Muriel fluttered out of the sack, right past Ginger's nose. Ginger snapped her jaws, just missing the moth. 'UURGH! What a revolting, moth-eaten old sack,' Ginger yelped, eyeballing Muriel as she escaped into the trees above.

The winded spies lay in a heap on the dusty floor.

Weasel was pretty ticked off. And being the fine, upstanding Woodlands creature he was, he felt he just had to say something.

'Ahem, excuse me?' Weasel said. 'This is no way to treat a gentleman super-spy and his dormouse chum. I shall have all your names and report you to the proper authorities!'

He pulled out a bicycle pump from beneath his jumper.

'Ah!' Rather embarrassed, he shoved it quickly back. After another dig around, he produced a pencil and notebook.

'Ready!' Weasel said, waiting for names, even though he sort of knew them anyway.

Ginger narrowed her eyes and Viv and Vic cringed. But to their surprise, Ginger replied in a sugary voice, 'I'm so sorry, what was I thinking?' She fluttered her eyelashes. 'What about some refreshments, a nice cup of tea, maybe a paw massage?'

'Well, yes, that's more like it!' Weasel nodded keenly.

Doorkins nudged him in the side. 'I don't think ...'

'Just a spot of milk in my tea, please, and maybe a custard cream or two. How about you, Doorkins?' Weasel went on.

Ginger began to rumble like a fiery volcano. Her eyes bulged and it looked as though she might erupt at any second.

Vic thought it best to step in before it all went off. He jammed the splurge gun right in Agent Weasel's snout.

UH-OH, thought Doorkins. *This could mean trouble ...*

When a weasel is in danger or gets threatened

– particularly with a splurge gun in the face –
this can cause a switch into what is known as
a Weasel War Dance. If you've never witnessed
a Weasel War Dance, it involves a great deal of
spinning, flipping, twisting and wild bottom-
shaking. It really is quite a spectacle, and it tends
to confuse or even hypnotise the enemy.

And Agent Weasel's bottom was starting to
shake!

Suddenly he flipped up, whacking the splurge
gun from Vic's paws, and sprang into full Weasel
War Dance mode. He waggled and rolled and
dived and spun. His display was so awesome the
foxes just stood and
gawped, even
Ginger.

DUH!

SPLURGE

WEASEL WAR
DANCE MODE

THWACK

VIC

A high triple flip caused Weasel's tail to brush Vic's nose. The tickle snapped Vic out of his hypnotic trance and he dived for the splurge gun.

'PACK IT IN OR THE DORMOUSE GETS IT!' Vic snarled, aiming the weapon at Doorkins's head.

With his friend in danger, Weasel brought his acrobatic display under control. Which was fortunate for the foxes, as he had been about to turn it up to full attack mode – and a ferocious weasel can be very hot to handle indeed, even for a bunch of big, tough foxes.

'Sorry, Weasel,' said Doorkins. 'Brilliant performance though!'

EEK!

Weasel half smiled – Weasel War Dances really took it out of you. But at least Vic had lowered the splurge gun and his best pal was OK.

He would have to control his weasel instincts – they could get a little out of paw every now and again. Which was not always a bad thing … but the Weasel War Dance was definitely not in the *WI6 Big Book of Spying*. H would be livid if she heard about it. But when had that ever worried Weasel before? Er … never!

'That was a-mazing!' Viv blurted out. 'You should be on *Woodland's Got Talent* – in fact, can I have your autograph?'

'ENOUGH OF THIS CLAPTRAP!' shrieked Ginger. She ordered Viv to roll Weasel up in prickly brambles so there'd be no more of that wriggling and a-jiggling nonsense.

'*OOO, OUCH, EEK!*' squealed Weasel.

'Time to meet the Big Boss!' Ginger said with a grin. And with that, the friends were dragged off towards the rather spooky tree in Dingy Dell ...

CHAPTER 10

The fox hideout was an absolute DUMP. Bashed-in drums leaked pools of suspicious-looking green gunge. Broken wooden crates stamped with 'DANGER' and 'DO NOT OPEN' littered the floor. And badly spelt graffiti was scrawled everywhere. 'FOXES ROOL', 'THE FFG FOUR EVER', 'THE BARMY FOX ARMIE', and so on. It was a complete and utter shambles.

Agent Weasel peeked out of his prickly bramble wrap as he scraped and bounced along the rough ground. He could just make out Doorkins tottering alongside with a splurge gun trained on his back. His poor chum looked a bit nervous. As Doorkins glanced over, Weasel gave his friend a comforting wink. Viv assumed it was for her and winked back with a dainty wave. Weasel smiled bashfully.

As they approached the old tree, he noticed a small door set into the trunk. Surely this was not the entrance to the foxes' lair – it didn't look half scary enough.

Painted in a bright glossy pink, the door had a fancy brass handle and a knocker in the shape of a neat wee pumpkin. A couple of well-tended hanging baskets completed the look. *Very odd decoration for a sinister hideout*, thought Weasel.

A sudden ruckus interrupted his thoughts. The fox twins had made a dash for the small door.

'OI, I'M FIRST!' cried Vic.

'NO, ME – OOW, GET OFF MY PAW, WILL YOU!' squealed Viv as they squeezed through the tiny doorway, crashing to the floor with a hefty *THUD*.

'What is wrong with you DUNDERHEADS?' Ginger fumed, as she stalked in, dragging the spies with her.

The inside of the tree was even more astonishing than the front door. It had been made into a remarkably cosy sitting room, with patterned rugs, comfy sofa and pretty pictures hanging on the wall.

Doorkins kind of liked it. It reminded him of his snug flat in the tree above Flaky-Bark Cottage. Apart from the fancy flowery-pink bits, it could be home!

'You two are acting like kindergarten cubs – it's so embarrassing!' scolded Ginger.

'AWWW, that's not fair, boss,' whined Viv. 'CAN I PULL THE LEVER, BOSS, CAN I?'

'NO, ME, I WAS FIRST!' yelled Vic.

Ginger slammed the front door and, with a look like thunder, stamped over to the fireplace. She took hold of a candlestick on the mantelpiece and pulled it down like a lever.

'AWWWWW!' chimed the twins in disappointment.

CLUNK, THUNK went a heavy noise far below, and the floor began to move steadily downwards, just as some cheesy elevator music started to play. *DEE—DA—DEE DI—DI—DA—DEE!*

Viv and Vic settled themselves on the big squashy sofa.

What a clever thing, thought Weasel, lying on the ground in the brambles. He watched the door disappear into darkness on the wall high above.

Then to everyone's shock, there came a *PAAAARP*. Somebody had trumped. Always a worry in an elevator!

The twins immediately pointed at Ginger, who looked down her snout with utter disgust, as if to say, 'Who, me? NEVER in a million years!' Viv grunted as she tried to hold in a giggle. Weasel and Doorkins shrugged, baffled by the mystery bottom squeak.

Fortunately it was quickly forgotten as the

elevator ground to a halt with a *CLUNK, CLANK.*

The jolt caused Doorkins to stagger, falling straight into Viv's lap. Viv smiled and stroked his little head affectionately … but Doorkins hardly noticed, because he was so astonished by the view that lay before them.

The elevator had come to rest on a high platform overlooking a cavernous hollow. Gigantic tree roots sprouted from the earth walls, and tunnels led off in all directions. The space was brightly lit by large tin factory lights hanging from the ceiling. Weasel squinted at them – he reckoned they'd been pinched from Farmer Garrett's chicken sheds … along with the odd hen, no doubt.

In the centre he could make out an impressive circular table, where fox minions were busily pushing marker pieces across a giant map of the United Woodlands. Others nattered away on an assortment of different coloured phones ... all hatching more devious plans, Weasel guessed.

'Welcome to the FFG control room!' said Viv proudly, pulling Agent Weasel to his feet by the bramble briars. *OUCH!*

Looking down the stairs from their platform, Weasel could see now that the cave was massive – more of a small town than a hideout. He began to wonder if they had bitten off a bit more than they could chew. Which for his dormouse friend was only about the size of a titchy hazelnut!

At the far end of the control room, a large banner showed a fierce fox head with the words 'FEENDISH FOX GANG' scrawled below.

Spelling really wasn't their strong point.

In front of the banner and facing away from Agent Weasel was a tall flowery-patterned swivel chair on a podium, with a pair of slender furry legs poking out. Who was in that chair? Weasel just had to know. Could it be the FFG's leader?

Leaning forward for a better view, Weasel heard a *CLANG* as he dropped something on the floor. It was Muriel's box, which had somehow worked its way out of Weasel's WI6 spy jumper.

Doorkins tried to reach it with the end of his fluffy dormouse tail.

'OOOOO, what's this?' said Viv, bending down to pick up the box and accidentally shoving her backside on to the prickly brambles.

'YEEEOOOW!' she shrieked, ramming straight into Weasel, who swayed dangerously at the top of stairs. As if in slow motion, he began to tip towards the control-room floor.

Doorkins dived for the brambles.

'OOOWW!' he cried, as the thorns slipped through his paws.

'Y-Y-YICKERTY Y-YIKES!' exclaimed Weasel as he bumped down the steep stairs.

BOSH! Taking out two fox minions, Weasel bounced up on to the map table, scattering the marker pieces everywhere. Foxes jumped left, right and centre to avoid the hurtling W16 furball.

Weasel smashed and crashed the whole length of the control room.

'OUCH, OOO, SORRY, OWW, PARDON ME!' he apologised as he went.

Doorkins covered his eyes – he couldn't bear to watch.

Eventually, Weasel thumped into a pair of unsuspecting fox minions and came to a stop in a big, spiky heap. There was much moaning and groaning as the animals tried to untangle themselves.

'ENOUGH!' barked a loud, commanding voice. All heads turned towards the podium as the swivel chair slowly rotated …

CHAPTER 11

Weasel would bet his hind paws on it: this just had to be the infamous FFG leader!

An elegant vixen perched in the high-backed swivel chair wearing a red military-style beret, pushed to a jaunty angle. She glared fiercely at Agent Weasel, stroking her big bushy tail like a beloved pet. All the other foxes seemed to cringe in her presence.

As Weasel stiffly dragged himself up, there was a gentle pat on his arm – Doorkins and the fox twins were directly behind him. They peeked fearfully over his shoulder, trying to look as small as possible (which was a bit tricky for Viv and Vic, each being the size of a modest box van).

Viv secretly pushed Muriel's wooden box back into Weasel's paw. *Aww, Viv's a good sort really,* he thought.

'Watch out!' Viv whispered from behind her paw. 'She's in a terrible mood. Always is, this time of year. That's why she ordered us to do all those horrible things to the United Woodlands animals. Because she's in a big grump!'

Hmmmm, interesting, pondered Weasel, twizzling his whiskers. *What was it about this time of year, that von ... von ... von Powder-Puff. No, von In-a-Huff ... von Had-Enough ... ?* It was no good, Weasel could not remember the name! *Better introduce myself quickly*, he thought.

'Ahem!' Weasel cleared his throat. He was about to do his 'My name is Weasel, Agent Weasel' thing, when the vixen held up a paw to silence him. She beckoned Ginger forward, frowning at her dishevelled state as Ginger leaned over to whisper in her boss's ear.

After a bit of nodding, scowling and some raised eyebrows, the boss sprang to her feet with such force that the chair swizzled round and knocked Ginger off the back of the podium.

Ginger grabbed for the huge FFG banner, but it pinged off its hangings and crashed to the ground with her. '*YEEOOW!*' she yelled with a *BOSH–BANG–CRUMP!*

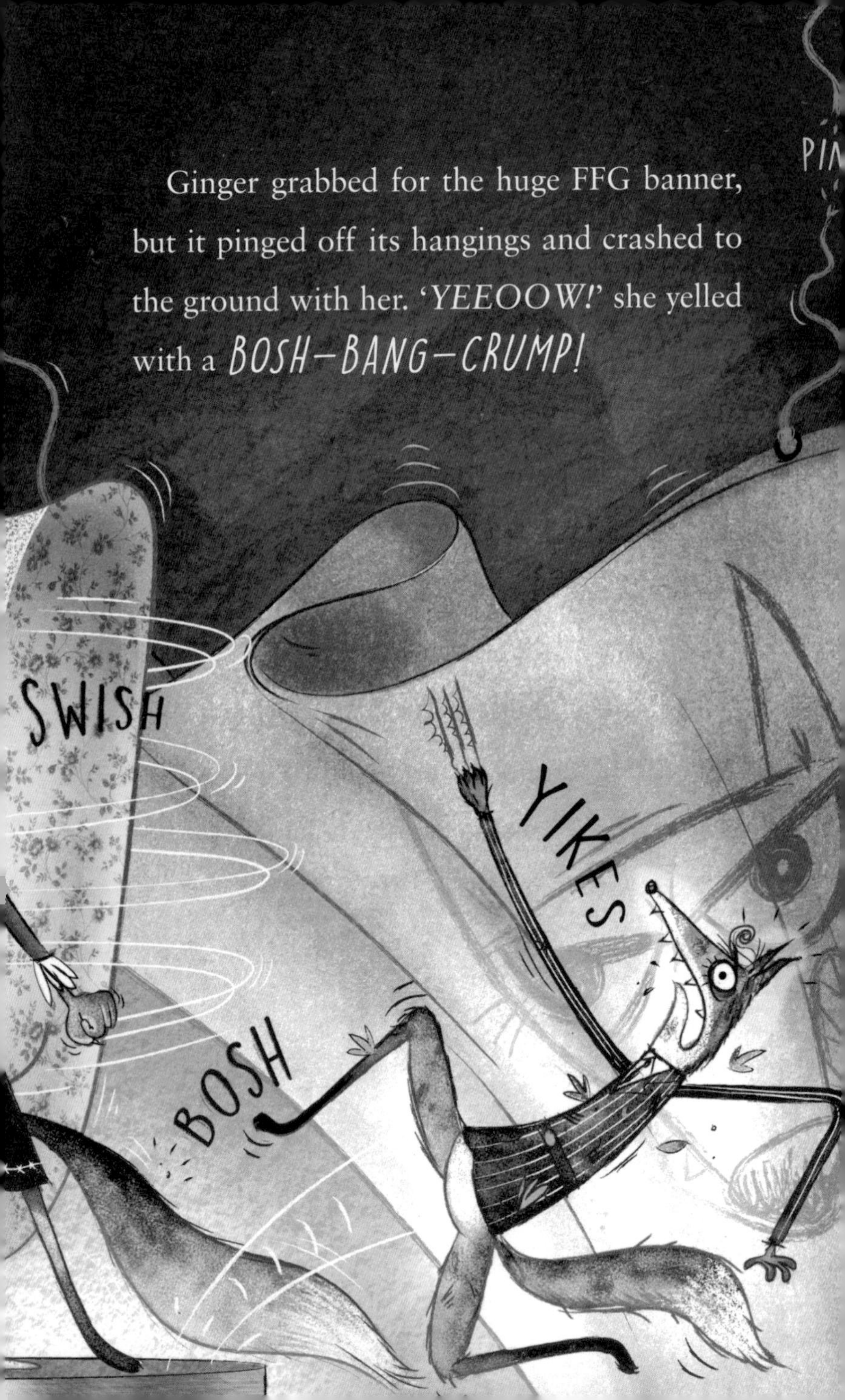

PIN

SWISH

YIKES

BOSH

Poor Ginger, it really wasn't her day.

The FFG boss looked at Agent Weasel as if he were a bad taste in her mouth. 'We meet at last, Weasel … or should I say Secret Agent Weasel of WI6 Woodland Intelligence? You dare to spy on the most feared gang in the United Woodlands, attack my loyal fox minions and wreck my gloriously evil control room!'

Hmmm, the control room wasn't entirely Weasel's fault. But he didn't want to get Viv in trouble, so he replied calmly.

'Well, one, spying is my job. Two, you guys *have* been just a little bit naughty. And three, how do you know my name? Because I can't for the life of me remember yours!'

'MY NAME,' she growled, 'is MADAM VIXEN VON FLUFF. And I am leader, kingpin, top dog of this operation!'

Very touchy, thought Weasel. Viv was right, this von Fluff certainly was in a rotten mood. He considered it best not to point out that she surely meant top fox, not top dog.

'You, Agent Weasel,' she sneered, strolling gracefully down the steps, 'are known to all decent hardworking crooks in the United Woodlands underworld. And it seems you are set on becoming a thorn in the FFG's side!'

'YAY for Agent Weasel!' yelled Doorkins in a brave voice. The fox minions began to snarl and slobber, moving in on the two captives with claws bared.

GRRRRRR

'SILENCE!' bellowed von Fluff, calling them off with a wave of her paw. 'And who, pray tell, is this?' She eyed the dormouse as though she might gobble him up at any moment.

'D-Doorkins, ma'am – f-fellow adventurer and best p-pal to the great Agent Weasel,' he stuttered nervously.

'Ah yes, I have heard of this … Doooorkins. Pesky sidekick, gardening columnist for the *Daily Conker* and *supposedly* the finest pumpkin grower in the United Woodlands,' she said, spitting the 'p' of pumpkin rather spitefully.

'Not supposedly, *actually*!' replied Doorkins proudly. 'Winner of the Best in Show Acorn Cup four years running at the Autumn Big Bash!'

Von Fluff gnashed her pointy teeth in a fearsome snarl.

'HA! The Autumn Big Bash,' she mocked viciously. 'I can tell you NOW you won't be winning anything this year, my furry little friend!'

'Ah, now I think you might be wrong there – this year's crop was quite superb—'

'SILENCE!' she bellowed. 'You will NOT win, because there will be NO Big Bash to win at. I have a dastardly plan to flatten the whole thing and everyone at it. MWA HA HA HAAA!' she cackled, in the way that evil masterminds do.

'No, you can't! What about my prize pumpkin— er, I mean, all those poor animals?' Doorkins corrected himself.

'You United Woodlands scum have had it too good for too long! Today will be my TRIUMPH!' she screeched.

'YEAH!' said Vic. Von Fluff flashed him a very hard stare and he looked down at the floor feeling a bit silly.

'Enough of this babble. Your time is up – and have we got a treat in store for you!' Von Fluff rubbed her paws together.

Ah! Maybe tea, biscuits and that paw massage, thought Weasel hopefully.

'TARRED and FEATHERED, TARRED and FEATHERED, TARRED and FEATHERED!' chanted the fox minions.

MAY-BEEEEEEEE not then! Weasel reconsidered.

Ginger, who had only just hauled herself out from behind the podium, scuttled over and whispered timidly in her boss's ear.

'WHAAAT?' von Fluff exclaimed. 'Ah, right. Don't panic, anyone. I have been informed that we are completely out of sticky black tar!'

'BOOOOOOOOOO!' protested the foxes.

'Must have used it up on that last batch of spies!' von Fluff muttered to Ginger out of the corner of her mouth. 'But never fear, my faithful minions – we will still have our TAR and FEATHERING!'

'HOORAY!' chimed the foxes.

'Our stores hold many jars of GLOOPY HONEY from our victorious robbery of the

Bee-licious Honey Works last week. It will do just as well.'

'YUM! Anything that involves honey is all right by me,' whispered Weasel in Doorkins's ear.

The foxes chittered with excitement. Von Fluff held up her paws for hush.

'These two shall be taken from here and dunked in stickiness, rolled in heaps of fluffy feathers, then tied up and dangled from the Creepy Tree – as a reminder to all that NOBODY MESSES WITH THE FIENDISH FOX GANG. MWA HA HA HAAA!'

The foxes went wild.

'GULP! They're going to turn us into freaky, fuzzy Christmas decorations!' flapped Doorkins.

'HMMMMM. This might put me off honey for life!' admitted Weasel.

CHAPTER 12

'BRING FORTH THE HONEY!' von Fluff hollered at Ginger.

Von Fluff's second in command scanned her fox crew. Viv and Vic were trying to keep a low profile behind the prisoners, but Ginger didn't miss them.

'YOU TWO!' she bawled, poking a paw at the fox twins. 'You know what to do!'

The pair looked deflated, knowing full well that they were the only dogsbodies in the gang. They trudged off to the food stores, mumbling and grumbling as they went.

By the time the twins arrived back, pushing a ramshackle shopping trolley jam-packed with honey, Weasel and Doorkins were dangling above a large, empty pickle jar.

'Nice view from up here, eh, Doorkins?' said Weasel brightly, trying to make the best of it.

'Yes – it's a very splendid evil control room, as evil control rooms go,' Doorkins replied. 'Do you think we'll get out of this sticky fix, Weasel?'

'That's just the point, Doorkins,' Weasel said, nodding at the stacks of honey jars. 'I think time might be on our side!'

Weasel was right. The foxes – well, just Viv and Vic – were now scrambling up and down a pair of ladders, pouring the little jars of honey into the huge jar. It was going to take hours, days, if not weeks to fill!

'Let's just hang around here and relax, my friend,' whispered Weasel. 'I'm sure help is on the way. Hey, I know, how about a cracking game to pass the time?'

Doorkins immediately seemed to doze off. *SNOOOOOOORE!*

Well, I never, thought Weasel. Was his pal trying to avoid a bit of harmless fun? No, Doorkins would never do that – the poor chap must be so tired.

Some time much, much later …

The honey was now somewhere up to knee level and the FFG were getting pretty bored and restless.

'Can't this go any faster?' asked an irritated von Fluff, lounging in her flowery swivel chair.

'Well, if anybody wants to help!' replied Viv in a rather ruffled manner.

All the other gang members looked away, trying to avoid eye contact.

'But you two are doing so magnificently!' said Ginger, as she reclined on the podium, picking bramble thorns and dried mud from her bushy tail. 'Why don't you finish the job on these two pesky spies, and we'll go and see to Operation Autumn Big Bash?'

'Ah, yes – what a brilliant idea!' agreed von Fluff.

Viv frowned.

'See that these irritating meddlers are properly dunked, gunked and feathered,' the fox leader told them. 'And no slacking, you two – remember, I have eyes everywhere!' Von Fluff jabbed a threatening paw towards the fox twins. 'Enjoy your sticky end, you bothersome fuzzballs. MWA HA HA HAAA,' she cackled.

The fox gang bustled off down the nearest tunnel, excited by the promise of putting another dastardly deed into action.

How rude, thought Weasel. *How very rude indeed!*

'AWWW, not again!' cried Vic. 'It's always

us – we're going to miss all the fun now.'

'FUN? It's not my idea of FUN!' barked Viv. 'I'm fed up to the back teeth of doing cunning, nasty things. Can't we just do something nice for a change?'

As the twins continued to squabble, two small, glossy black creatures scuttled in through a crack in the ceiling. They proceeded past the bickering foxes and straight towards the dangling captives.

Chomp-chomp-gnaw, chomp-chomp-gnaw ...

What is that noise? thought Weasel, as Doorkins jolted awake beside him.

'SSSSHHHHH!' whispered a small but firm voice behind them. 'Stag Beetle Special Operations Regiment here. Don't worry, we'll have you free in a jiffy!'

Good old Muriel must have got through, thought Weasel. These stag guys were legends. They specialised in rescue from sticky ends – the ones that secret agents always seemed to get themselves into!

Weasel strained to look over his shoulder … and saw a pair of stag beetles speedily munching through the ropes with their powerful pincers.

'OI! What's all this whispering?' grumbled Vic, plodding back up a ladder in a real big sulk, carrying yet another single jar of honey.

'Just a bit of a sniffle – I'm … allergic to honey fumes,' replied Doorkins.

'Really?' Vic said, not actually knowing what 'allergic' meant.

'Yes – and if I get even the tiniest sniff of a feather, I come out in all sorts of horrible

SCUTTLE
SCUTTLE

lumps and bumps!' kidded Weasel.

'EEEW!' said Vic.

Suddenly, Weasel's paws were free. The beetles had managed to gnaw through his bonds! Flipping upside down, Weasel wrapped his legs around the rope above.

'HEY!' cried Vic, lunging out over the pickle jar where Weasel had been just a moment ago.

'MUUUUUUUUUUMMY!' Vic howled, plunging down to the honey below with a SPLAAAATCH!

The jar began to rock wildly as Vic squirmed around in the gooey mess. Weasel leapt for the glass rim, but a sudden jolt flung him over the side.

Hmmm, this is probably not going to end well, thought Weasel, as the ground rapidly approached …

POOOOOOF! Weasel landed, but there was no pain!

He opened his eyes and everything was tickly and white. *I must be in paradise,* he thought dreamily.

'AAAAAACHOOO!' Ah no – only one thing made him sneeze like that. He poked his head up, right in the middle of a large basket stuffed with fluffy feathers. 'AAAAAACHOOO!'

'That was jolly close!' called a rather striking stag beetle perched on the basket edge. 'I'm Steadfast, Corporal Steadfast.' She held out one of six legs, which Weasel shook gratefully.

'Ah, Agent Weasel – glad to see you in one piece.' It was the second beetle, the legendary Commander Stalwart, leader of the Stag Beetle Special Operations Regiment. He hopped up next to Corporal Steadfast, plucking a feather from his impressive-looking pincers.

'You guys are awesome – I'm an enormous fan!' said Weasel. 'Let me introduce you to my good friend Door—'

'WEEEEASEL!' came a frantic cry from above.

To Weasel's shock, Doorkins was still dangling over the massive pickle jar – on a partially chewed rope! The stag beetles must have forgotten him in their rush.

And the huge jar was beginning to tip, as a very gloopy Vic tried to claw his way up the inside. *CREEEEEAK!* went the jar, crashing down towards the basket and the WI6 agents …

All three scattered, diving for safety.

But then – *PING!* Weasel looked up as

Doorkins's rope snapped and he plummeted to the floor. It would be impossible to reach him in time! Weasel covered his eyes, waiting for the unavoidable *SPLAT* ...

CHAPTER 13

It gradually began to dawn on Doorkins that he was not splatted on the control room floor … but safe and sound in Viv's beefy paws. Viv had dived, arms outstretched, and caught the dormouse in the nick of time.

Before Doorkins could give his thanks, a loud 'HEEEELP-ELP-ELP-ELP!' echoed through the vast fox den.

'VIC!' yelled Viv in concern. Everyone dashed over to the source of the cry, somewhere near the large upturned pickle jar.

Poor Vic. There he was, covered from head

to tail in goo and feathers. Weasel and the beetles were trying to heave him out of the basket, but Viv flopped limply back in and started bawling like a little cub.

'WAAAAHH AAAAH! I d-don't like b-being 'orrible really. W-when you're big, ugly and smell like m-mouldy cheese, nobody wants to be your f-friend! Anyways, all I wanted was some pudding – WAAHAAAAA!'

The group exchanged worried looks.

'Now, come on, big fella – it'll all be fine,' soothed Weasel, patting Vic's icky paw. 'You can have pudding three times a day at the WI6 Hedgequarters canteen! Anything from chestnut-syrup crumble to juicy goose-gog pie!'

'Honest?' sniffed Vic noisily, suddenly brightening up.

'Honest and cross my heart,' said Weasel.

A wide, creepy and very toothy grin spread across Vic's face. Doorkins winced – with that smile, Vic should definitely stick to frowning!

It was time to get a wriggle on. Von Fluff had a big head start, and they needed to get out of this spooky den and foil her cunning plan.

Weasel hoped the fox twins might be able to guide them out, but unfortunately they didn't have a clue. The sitting-room elevator had disappeared back into the ceiling and no one knew how to get it down again.

'We're just a pair of dogsbodies,' said Viv. 'Nobody tells us anything!'

'There is that other spy though,' said Vic from his basket, doing an excellent impression of an enormous fluffy chick in its nest.

'Spy? What spy?' asked Weasel.

'She's one of your lot – erm … Agent something?' said Viv. 'They've got her in the super-dooper high-security lockdown cell, suspended above a pike-infested underground stream!'

Agent Weasel looked at Doorkins for help. 'A pike is a large, scary fish with lots of sharp teeth,' murmured his friend. 'It could easily munch up a WI6 team in a single gulp!'

'Hmmm, sounds tricky,' said Commander Stalwart, tweaking his left antenna. 'HANG ON! This prisoner couldn't be the one and only …Agent Mole? She's been missing in action for days!'

'Ha! That was it – AGENT MAUL!' said Viv. 'Knew I'd remember!'

Stalwart flashed a frown at the big vixen. Mole was one of Woodland Intelligence's finest, and a brilliant underground specialist. If you were stuck in a deep, dark hole, she could most definitely get you out of it.

That was it then – they had a plan:

Find Agent Mole.

Stage a rescue.

Get out of the fiendish fox den and straight off to the Big Bash – quick smart. Before it got … er … smashed!

'This is where I take my leave,' announced Commander Stalwart. 'More agents to save from sticky ends, don't you know. Corporal Steadfast will stay and help with your mission – she's our best beetle!'

'SIR!' Steadfast snapped to attention and saluted. So did all the other animals, kind of caught up in the moment.

With a return salute, Stalwart scuttled off, straight up the wall and through the tiny crack in the ceiling.

'OOOO! This is very exciting!' squealed Viv, clapping her big paws together.

'I think it's this way to the cell,' said Vic, already waddling off down a tunnel – keen to get on with things and off to the splendid-sounding WI6 canteen for some pudding.

They all followed his trail of downy feathers into the gloom.

A little while later ...

Vic seemed to be a bit lost. Weasel suspected he was more used to following than leading. How could they possibly find their way to Agent Mole in this rabbit warren of a fox den?

Vic scratched his chin, squinting into the dark before them.

PING! Suddenly, an idea popped into

Weasel's head. He rummaged around in his WI6-issue spy jumper and brought out a large … cheese grater.

'Ah no, not right at all!' He tried again, eventually pulling out a Y-shaped stick. 'Ah-ha!'

It didn't look like it would be particularly useful to anybody.

'Are you sure that's going to help, Weasel?' Doorkins asked his super-spy pal.

'If we're going to find Agent Mole, Doorkins, we need to locate the underground stream,' replied Weasel. 'This simple-looking stick can actually detect water – it's called a "divining rod", and this is an especially good one.'

He held the stick out by the two ends of the Y and it instantly began to waggle, pulling Weasel to the left and off down a narrow tunnel.

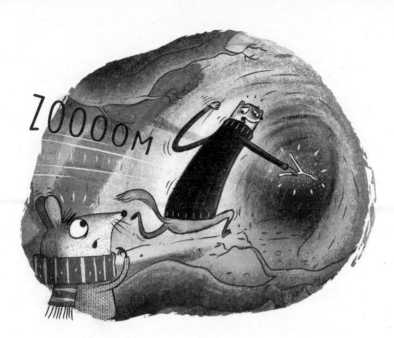

'Come on, team, no time to waaaaaaaaste …!' he called, disappearing from sight. Doorkins dashed after him and Viv, Vic and Steadfast followed in quick pursuit.

As they continued, the tunnel seemed to get smaller, darker and impossibly steep. They could hear a distant *SWOOSH* of flowing water. It felt as though they must be on the right track.

Poor Vic was lagging behind by quite a way. His itchy feathers were driving him crazy!

'Guys, wait for me!' he called. 'I honestly can't see a— OOOOOPS!' He tripped on a sticky-up root and went rolling down the tunnel, picking up speed as he went.

'STOP!' said Weasel, holding a paw to his ear. 'Can anyone else hear that rumbling noise?'

'Hmmmm. Could be the water up ahead?' suggested Corporal Steadfast, unaware of the fast-approaching Vic.

'LOOOOK OOOUT!' The yell came from behind and – *BOFFFFF!* – Vic bowled into the other animals as if they were a bunch of skittles. And off they all went, sliding down the steep passage.

'WEEEEEEEEEEEEEEEE!' cried Corporal

RUMBLE,

RUMBLE

WEEEEEE

Steadfast,
who seemed
to be rather
enjoying it.

'AAAAAAAAAAAA
AAAAARGGGGHH!'
went the others, who were not!

They plunged on, the sound of
rushing water appearing to get closer

Viv, who was hurtling along at the front, stuck her claws into the earth walls. Just as they reached the tunnel's end, she managed to bring the animals to a grinding halt.

'PHEW! Quick thinking, Viv!' said Weasel. Viv beamed proudly.

Weasel carefully leaned out of the tunnel opening. GULP! It was a long way down – he could just make out the bubbling water in the shadows below.

YEEEOOW

Drawing back from the edge, he noticed his divining rod sticking out of the tunnel's ceiling.

'OOO, must have that back!' And without thinking, Weasel plucked it out of the wall.

Now, was that another faint rumble he could hear?

Suddenly, a web of cracks spread from the hole where the stick had been stuck.

Hmmmmm, thought Weasel. *I get the feeling this is not going to end well.*

With a crumbling roar, the tunnel's end collapsed and the group of rather surprised animals plummeted towards the water below.

CHAPTER 14

The jumble of animals plunged into the water with a great *SPLAAASH!*

It was so inky black down there, it took a moment to figure out the right way up.

Weasel popped up first, gasping and spluttering in the icy cold. The dark was so echoey and endless. It made him feel quite small and alone.

Then, one after the other, his friends bobbed to the surface too ... *plop-plop-plop-plop*. Weasel certainly felt a little warmer to know they were there.

He gazed around. The underground stream flowed through a long, open tunnel, with the earth wall they had just taken a tumble down on one side and a raised bank on the other. The bank looked easy enough to scrabble up, but he couldn't quite see over its top.

By far the most interesting thing was a rusty chain running straight up out of the water and disappearing into the murky darkness above.

Might this chain lead to Agent Mole? pondered Weasel, twizzling his whiskers. It was definitely worth a shinny up there to find out.

But his team must come first. 'R-right, let's c-count heads,' he shivered. 'One, that's me, t-two, three ... Where's V-Vic?'

Vic was doggy-paddling in circles, trying his absolute best not to go under.

'Ah, Vic, there you are … f-four. We have one m-missing. There should be five of us!' gasped Weasel.

'YOOHOOO!'

They all looked up.

High above, Corporal Steadfast waved from the edge of the tunnel opening – or what was left of it.

She flexed her knees, ready to dive. Taking a graceful hop, she launched herself into the air. With a double somersault and a series of nimble twists she plopped into the water, making barely a ripple. It was magnificent! As she bobbed to the surface, everybody clapped.

'That's a ten from me!' cried Doorkins, flapping his tiny paws to stay afloat.

'OI! Who touched my leg?' asked Viv. 'Is

it you, Vic? Are you trying to give me the collywobbles?'

But Vic was nowhere near his sister. He was paddling around on his back, still desperately trying to stay afloat.

Without warning, an enormous silver tail flicked above the surface, right in front of Weasel's snout.

SPUUURLOSH! It crashed back down, giving everyone a spluttering faceful of water. The animals all blinked in shock.

'PIKE!' they screeched, making a mad dash for the bank.

With the big fish lurking somewhere between Weasel and the others, he decided to swim for the rusty chain, hoping to lead the pike away from his team.

Paddling like bonkers, Weasel could sense

something huge ploughing through the water behind him.

'SWIM, WEASEL, SWIM!' the others called desperately, having made it to the bank opposite.

What do they think I'm doing – taking a relaxing bath? Weasel frantically grabbed for the chain and scrambled upwards. And only just in time.

Two huge silvery-green fish leapt from the water, missing Weasel by a whisker!

With a big soggy SLAP, their heads bashed together and they sank into the inky blackness. Weasel clung on more tightly than ever.

SPLATCH

'OI! WHO'S THERE?' came a gruff foxy voice from up on the bank. The rescue team froze.

'Hmmmm, must be those daft fish – probably trying to eat each other again!' said the voice, wandering away from where Doorkins, Steadfast and the fox twins were crouching.

Doorkins cautiously peeked up to see a tall fox guard swaggering over to a rickety wooden table, a dreaded splurge gun in his paws. Sitting at the table was a second fox – a vixen, reading the *Daily Conker* newspaper.

Ah, fabulous, thought Doorkins. *Wonder if she caught my article 'Top Tips for Giant Pumpkin Growing'? Probably not,* he sighed. *She'll be reading about daring robberies or car chases.*

'It's right horrible being down here, guarding this cell!' grumbled the tall fox as he glanced around nervously. 'It gives me the creeps!'

'I don't like it any more than you do. But the boss says this Agent Mole needs watching twenty-four seven. Very dangerous, apparently,' replied the vixen, not looking up from her paper.

Weasel, who was now aware of the fox guards chattering away on the bank, tried to stay as still as a mouse. Squinting into the darkness above, he could just make out what looked like a metal cube. It was about the size of Doorkins's garden shed and attached to four chains, one of them being the chain Weasel was clinging to for dear life.

This just had to be Mole's super-dooper secure whatsit cell. Weasel would need to clamber up there, while avoiding a splat from that vicious splurge gun.

Meanwhile, the others were hatching a plan of their own. Corporal Steadfast stood to attention, saluted the others and plopped straight back into the freezing water. She motored across to Weasel and scuttled up the chain, as quick as a ferret up a trouser leg.

Doorkins, Viv and Vic carefully tiptoed along the bank towards the fox guards.

'YEEEOOOOW-SHIVERING-SALMON-SCALES!' came Weasel's unexpected cry from the middle of the stream.

'WHO GOES THERE?' yelled the vixen guard, shining a powerful searchlight towards the din.

And what a sight! A huge pike had clamped its jaws on to the bottom of Weasel and Steadfast's chain, joggling them around in a ferocious manner.

'SPIES! SPLURGE 'EM!' growled the vixen. The tall fox took aim.

'MOOOOOOOAAAHHH!' went a spine-tingling groan from the bank.

The fox with the splurge gun was so alarmed, he fired a shot. *SPLAT!* The gooey missile went wildly off target, striking the thrashing pike right in the gills and making it sink back underwater.

With another '*MOOOOOOAAAHHH!*' a monstrous feathery swamp creature lumbered out of the dark, heading straight for the two fox guards. The terrified pair turned and scarpered down the nearest tunnel, screeching as they went.

'HA! That sorted those two out – brilliant work, Vic,' cheered Weasel from his wobbly chain.

Vic beamed from ear to ear.

Oooh, that grin again, Doorkins thought with a shudder. He patted the bedraggled, feathery fox on the back. 'Well done, old chum ... YUCK!' Doorkins shook the mess of feathers off his paw in disgust.

'No problem,' said Vic. 'If it gets us closer to having some pudding, it's fine by me!'

There was a yell from above.

'Bit dark up here – could we have a little help?' called Weasel. He and Steadfast were climbing the chain to investigate.

Viv aimed the foxes' abandoned searchlight towards the tunnel's ceiling. It revealed the metal cube and, sticking out between some bars ... was a twitching pink snout!

'Agent Mole, is that you?' asked Weasel as they clambered up to the roof of the cell.

'YES, WEASEL – THIS IS AGENT MOLE!' she called. 'Good to hear your voice. Can't see you all that well – those fox ruffians took my specs!'

Poor Agent Mole was as blind as a bat without her glasses. But her other super-mole senses – touch, smell, taste and hearing – more than made up for that. And when underground she didn't really need sight at all.

'Don't worry, we'll have you out in two shakes of a squirrel's tail,' Weasel said confidently.

While Corporal Steadfast checked the roof for booby traps, Weasel inspected the door. Instead of a normal lock, there was a large red button with big capital letters saying: 'RELEASE ME'. *Well, that's what we want to do, isn't it?* thought Weasel, stretching out his paw to press it.

'Oh, by the way, Weasel,' said Mole urgently. 'Whatever you do, don't press the big red—'

CLICK!

Too late!

CLUNK, the cell door swung open.

'Ah! Splendid,' said Weasel.

'The big red button's the booby trap!' shrieked Mole.

PING, PING, PING, PING went the four chains, as they popped off the cell.

'OOPS!' blurted Weasel, as they began to fall ...

CHAPTER 15

The cell jolted to an abrupt stop. Mole leaned out of the door, desperately clinging on to Weasel's front paw as he dangled over the drop.

'C-can't hold this for long!' strained Steadfast. The two spies looked up.

The plucky corporal had taken the full weight of the hefty cell. Her pincers were clamped to the chain above, and she'd hooked a couple of legs around a ring on the roof. She was remarkably strong for such a tiny creature. In fact, stag beetles can lift over two hundred times their own weight. And if you've ever tried to heave two or three fully grown elephants over your head, you'll know that's quite a lot!

But the cumbersome metal cube was proving a bit much even for Corporal Steadfast. Beads of sweat appeared on her beetly brow as the chain began to slip from her grasp.

'We're going to have to dive for it!' yelled Mole.

'REALLY? But it's a long way DOOOOOOOOOOOOWN!' Weasel cried, as Mole pitched out of the doorway.

The two WI6 agents plummeted to the water below.

Hmmmm! She's very daring, thought Weasel as he tumbled downwards. *But I've done this before and know just how chilly that stream is!*

SPLASH! SPLOSH! They hit the water one after the other, Weasel doing a rather impressive but painful belly flop.

'OUCH! Er ... thanks for that, Mole!' gasped Weasel, bobbing to the surface.

'My p-pleasure, Weasel, so pleased you hit the water and not that m-muddy bank ... Couldn't see a thing when I let g-go – no specs, you know!' Mole said, stuttering with the cold.

Weasel raised his eyebrows, thinking how disastrous it really could have been.

From behind them came a low fishy growl.

'Oh no, not again!' spluttered Weasel.

He paddled round just in time to see a gaping mouth full of razor-sharp teeth.

The pike was back! Weasel had to admit that it was very determined. He scrunched up his eyes, expecting to be completely munched up.

Then ... *SMASH–BASH–SPLAAASH!*

Weasel blinked open one eye. Surprisingly, he was in one piece, and so was Mole. And right where the huge ravenous pike had been, the shed-sized metal cube was sinking beneath the water.

'Sorry, chaps – it sort of slipped,' said Corporal Steadfast, standing heroically on the cell's roof.

'YAAAAY!' the others whooped from the bank.

'Steadfast, you legend!' cheered Vic.

As Mole and Weasel dragged themselves from the water, Viv stuck out a hulking great paw to Mole.

'My name's Viv, nice to meet—' But before she could finish, Viv found herself flying over Mole's shoulder ... then *SPLATCH* into the squelchy bankside mud.

Without her specs, Mole had seen this huge orange blur as an enemy fox – and her super-spy reactions had kicked in. Just as she was about to deliver a rock-buster stun-blow (a classic WI6 fighting move), Weasel dived to the rescue.

'STOP! Mole, please don't bash Viv, she's one of us!' he exclaimed, holding back Viv's lethal shovel-shaped paws.

'SQUIGGLING EARTHWORMS!' cried Mole. 'Sorry, Viv. Forgive me – never seen a WI6 fox before!'

'It's a long story!' Weasel told Mole, helping the dazed and muddy fox to her feet. 'One to discuss over tea and biscuits later.'

'PUUUUUDDING!' Vic yelled.

They all turned to stare at the fox.

'Pudding first, *then* tea and biscuits!' Vic

blurted, giving Weasel a particularly hard foxy stare.

'Another WI6 fox, I presume?' asked Mole, rather nonplussed. The others just rolled their eyes.

'Pilchard!' spat Viv, cuffing Vic round the head.

'OWWW!' he whinged.

'Ahem! Right, chaps,' said Mole. 'I expect you want out of here?' Everybody nodded eagerly. 'I know just the route – so let's get cracking!'

'HURRAH!' they all cheered, scuttling off after the WI6 underground specialist and down yet another damp and rather spooky tunnel.

As they made their way through the darkness, Weasel caught sight of a flickering glow up ahead. *Daylight at last*, he thought – it reminded him of the low autumn sun, dappling through the trees at Flaky-Bark

Cottage … *Ah, bliss! The sooner we get out of this gloomy dump, the better!*

But moving closer, he realised it was just a partly open door, painted in the same twee pink as the den entrance. A blue light glowed around its edges, and in its centre was a large, shiny plaque with 'THE BOSS' in raised letters.

'Well, no prizes for guessing whose evil lair this might be,' said Weasel.

But Vic had turned very pale indeed.

'Vic, are you all right?' asked Doorkins, rather concerned.

Vic trembled, his eyes wide.

'It's just – whenever we were in trouble, we got brought here for a good telling-off!' Viv piped up. 'Von Fluff gave us some right roastings in there. Vic's never really got over it.'

'Poor old Vic,' Steadfast said, giving the fox a gentle pat on the paw.

Suddenly a loud *CREEEEEAAAK* made them jump out of their skins.

'SOOORRY!' apologised Weasel. He'd pushed open the pink door, which seemed to have its own built-in creepy sound effect.

Weasel cautiously tiptoed in and they all followed, with poor Vic cowering at the back.

CHAPTER 16

The evil lair was *super-villain* meets *super-fluffy*. There were big swirly rugs, piles of flowery cushions, draped velvety fabrics and all sorts of fancy knick-knacks.

The blue flickery light they'd seen in the tunnel came from an impressive wall of TV screens set behind a grand oak-stump desk. It gave what would have been a quite cosy and welcoming room a more shadowy, menacing sort of feel. More suitable for a criminal mastermind.

Each screen showed live footage of an important spot in the United Woodlands.

There was Hedgequarters, Principal Pine Marten's residence and the site of the Big Bash – where all seemed fine and dandy. Animals were skipping about in the crisp autumn sunshine, with no sign of trouble.

But what was this? On the right-paw side of the screen was … FLAKY–BARK COTTAGE!

Shocked, Weasel plonked into the chair behind the grand oak-stump desk. He couldn't help but notice a rather splendid scrapbook lying in front of him. The cover had pink fur and sparkly bits stuck all over it, and in big, glittery letters it said 'TOP SECRET!'

Should he open it? It felt a bit naughty, looking at someone's private things. But it could contain very important information – even if it was big, pink and fluffy.

CRAAAAAASH! Vic broke Weasel's

concentration, clobbering around like a nervous elephant and knocking over fancy knick-knacks. The others tried to calm the flapping fox down. *Well*, reasoned Weasel, *if Vic's smashing all the fancy knick-knacks, might as well take a look at this sparkly scrapbook.*

He opened it carefully. It appeared to be full of *Daily Conker* newspaper cuttings.

BADGER SHAVED IN DESPICABLE BARE-BOTTOM CAPER!

RABBITS TWITCHY IN ITCHING POWDER PANDEMONIUM!

Then one particular cutting caught Weasel's eye. It was a picture of his good pal Doorkins, beaming next to one of his huge prize pumpkins. The headline read:

CONKER'S OWN WINS BIG BASH BEST IN SHOW!

Someone had written 'BOOOOO!' next to it in big black letters, and drawn a curly moustache and specs on Doorkins's proud chops!

'What do we have here, then?' said Doorkins over Weasel's shoulder. Weasel nearly jumped out of his fur, he was so startled.

A look of horror spread across Doorkins's face. 'B-but that's me!' he said, pointing a shaky paw at the vandalised photo.

Weasel noticed a piece of paper poking from the back of the scrapbook. He pulled it out cautiously.

WITHERING RAGWEED! It was an entry form for the Autumn Big Bash Best in Show competition. All of Madam Vixen von Fluff's details were filled in: name, date of birth, address, job. For job, she had written 'Criminal Mastermind', and someone had circled it in red pen. At the bottom of the form was a big stamp that read: 'REJECTED!'

'HA! This is why she wants to flatten the Big Bash!' exclaimed Weasel.

'They REJECTED her from Best in Show!' said Doorkins. 'She wants REVENGE!'

Weasel flopped back in disbelief.

The chair made an unmistakable *CLICK!*

A heavy scraping noise rumbled behind them. Viv, Vic and Steadfast, who were placing knick-knacks back on the shelves, stopped to stare in wonder.

Weasel and Doorkins swivelled round to see what the others were gawping at. The TV wall had trundled off to one side, revealing an incredible sight.

Sunlight streamed into a deep cave from a glass dome in the ceiling above. Weasel's gaze followed the dusty shaft of light to a podium below. And there, in all its plump, orangey splendour, sat a huge pumpkin.

Doorkins was speechless. In all his days he had never seen anything like it. A small tear came to his eye.

Had the infamous fox leader created this? She must be extraordinarily green-pawed.

Things were starting to make sense. Weasel twizzled his whiskers as a plan began to form in his super-spy brain.

TA-DA!

'Listen up, team!' he said urgently. 'I'm sure we can turn this whole thing around. Mole and I will go after the foxes and stick a rather annoying thistle in their plans. You guys get this plumptious pumpkin to the fair ASAP – it could be the key to von Fluff's grumpy mood!'

'But how, Weasel?' asked Doorkins. 'It's colossal!'

'You'll figure it out, old chum – I'm relying on you!' Weasel cried, dashing towards the door.

'HEY, there are my specs!' yelled Mole, grabbing her glasses from the desk as she bolted past.

AGENT MOLE'S SPECS

'But ... Weasel!' cried Doorkins.

Oh dear. It was no good – the agents had well and truly skedaddled!

CHAPTER 17

Mole bombed along the tunnel after her speedy super-agent colleague.

'ER ... WEASEL, YOOHOO!' she called. Bungling on her specs, she was just in time to see his tail whip around the corner ahead.

Weasel had come to a complete stop and Mole clobbered into him at full speed with an

ARRGGGH—BAAASH—OOOOF!

'OOOOO! Sorry, Weasel,' she groaned. 'Wasn't expecting you to brake so suddenly!'

'It just came to me,' he mumbled, lying snout down in the dirt with Mole on his back.

'I have absolutely no idea where I'm going!'

'I was trying to point that out, Weasel.' Mole was a bit disgruntled. 'There's a secret part of the den where these scoundrels prepare and launch all their devilish plans. And by the hair on my twitchy-twitch nose, I can sense it's thataway!' Mole pointed back up the tunnel.

'Ah, apologies, Mole, I do get carried away!' Weasel admitted. They pulled themselves up, dusted each other off and dashed off down the tunnel – this time, with Mole leading the way.

Meanwhile, back in Vixen von Fluff's evil lair ...

The 'get the pumpkin to the fair' team were in a bit of a jam. Lifting the enormous pumpkin was proving impossible, even with a super-strong stag beetle and two mammoth foxes.

Doorkins's eyeballs bulged as he strained to shift it. Powerlifting wasn't really a dormouse thing, but at least he was having a go. Vic, on the other paw, had given up completely and moped off into a dark corner.

'VIC, we need some help here!' growled Viv impatiently.

Vic just looked up miserably and muttered

something about, 'Definitely not getting any pudding now.' He plonked himself down on a small boulder, head in paws, and sulked.

'Let's think about this,' suggested Doorkins. 'There must be an easier way—'

But before he could finish, a low grating rumble came from Vic's direction. It sounded like his stomach, but the noise was actually coming from the boulder he had just sat down on. It was slowly sinking into the floor.

RUMBLE
RUMBLE

There was an ear-splitting *SQUEAK–SQUEAK–SQUEAK* from far above, as the glass dome drew back. With a *CLANK* and a shudder, the pumpkin podium began to rise up towards the daylight.

'YIPPEEE!' yelled Doorkins, racing to the podium to join Viv and Steadfast. 'Jump up, Vic – you big, clever fox, you!'

Back in the heart of the foxes' den …

Weasel and Mole peeked over a mound of earth at the end of their tunnel.

'This is the FFG's fiendish workshop,' whispered Mole.

Before them was a long, hollow lamp-lit den. Chains and pulleys hung down from the ceiling and there was a jumbled mess of sacks, crates, steel drums and other untidiness.

'It looks like we might have missed the crafty scallywags!' said Weasel, pointing to a mash of chunky tyre tracks in the den's earth floor.

The two WI6 agents tiptoed through the foxes' clutter, avoiding yucky pools of sticky gloop and abandoned tufts of badger fur. Weasel shivered, thinking of those poor chilly bare-bottomed creatures.

'Weasel, take a look at this!' Mole stood at a large drawing board, leafing through an unruly mess of files and papers.

'HMMMMMM! Sketches and workings-out for von Fluff's despicable plans, no doubt,' said Weasel, looking over Mole's shoulder.

There were some very strange scribbles indeed. One showed a boxy black and white collie dog, with wheels where the legs should be, and another was a map of Farmer Garrett's field. In the drawings – which were actually quite good, Weasel had to admit

– two of the wheeled dogs were advancing on a flock of petrified-looking sheep. A big black arrow pointed through the field's gate and straight towards the site of the Autumn Big Bash!

'WALLOPING WOOL-WORRIERS!' Weasel cried, putting two and two together. 'This is von Fluff's revenge plan. She's going to flatten the fair by stampeding a flock of Farmer Garrett's sheep right through it!'

'We need to follow these tracks,' said Mole. 'They must have disguised the FFG trucks as sheep dogs, using this badger fur and glue. How low can you get?'

'If we can delay the rotters, it might give the others time to get von Fluff's pumpkin to the Big Bash!' Weasel said.

'Yes, remind me why we're doing that

again?' asked Mole.

But Weasel had already shot off down the nearest tunnel.

'I wish he wouldn't do that,' sighed Mole, speeding after him.

Following the tyre marks, Weasel rounded a corner at full sprint, not seeing the dead end straight ahead and ... *SMACK!* Oh dear, he was on the floor – again.

'HEY! Can you stop bolting off like that?' grumbled Mole as she scurried around the corner. 'It's just ... Oh, sorry, are you all right?'

'UUUUUUH!' groaned Weasel.

'Hey, what's this?' said Mole, snatching a note pinned to the earth wall. She read it out loud:

Dear Annoying WI6 Pests,

If you are reading this, you've probably
  escaped our devious sticky end, BOOOOOO!
But we don't care, because you'll never catch us.

  All the best,
      Vixen von Fluff and the Gang
                                    XX

PS We've blocked off the tunnel – so you
really are stuffed now! MWA HA HA HAA!

'Well, that hurts my feelings!' said a rather flabbergasted Weasel.

'RIGHT!' said Mole, flexing her large shovel-shaped paws until they cracked. 'Enough's enough. Get behind me, Agent Weasel, it's DIGGING TIME!'

The tunnel filled with a blizzard of dirt. Weasel dived behind Mole as she burrowed speedily into the earth.

CHAPTER 18

FLUUUMP! Mole and Weasel burst out of the ground in a shower of soil and roots.

'That was A-MAZING, Mole,' said Weasel, taking a deep breath of fresh woodland air.

'Oh, it was nothing, really – digging is the best fun there is. Hey, what's that noise? Someone's coming!' she whispered urgently.

There was a *CRUUUNCH–CRUNCH CRUUUNCH–CRUNCH* sound, getting closer and closer. The pair leapt behind a nearby log, crouching low.

'OI, watch my paw, moss-for-brains. You nearly ran over it – again!' snapped a familiar voice.

'Well, if you'd just try walking in a straight line for once, instead of staggering about everywhere ...'

It was the wonderful sound of Viv and Vic bickering.

Weasel and Mole popped out from behind the log. There were their companions, rolling the giant pumpkin ahead of them. The fox twins were so happy to see their two agent friends that, without thinking, they let go of the pumpkin and it began to tip over …

'LOOK OUT!' yelled Mole.

Doorkins was standing beneath the pumpkin, completely unaware of the peril.

Corporal Steadfast bounded in, shoving the dormouse to safety. Then … *BOOOOUF* – the enormous pumpkin crashed down on the plucky stag beetle.

The animals gasped in shock.

'NOOOOOOOOOOO!' cried Doorkins, as he scrambled to lift the immense vegetable.

Weasel raced over to his pal and together they heaved … but in vain.

'NAARAAAARH!' came a tiny, muffled roar. And as the roar began to rise, so did the pumpkin.

There stood Steadfast, as strong as an oak tree, holding the mighty pumpkin above her head. Which was only five or six centimetres off the ground – but nonetheless, very impressive.

She certainly was the most ASTOUNDING beetle.

'Well, what are we waiting for, chaps?' Steadfast said matter-of-factly. 'OOOOOO … hang on, a little help please!' she yelled as her legs began to buckle.

The other animals sprang to her aid, managing to heave the gigantic pumpkin back on to its side.

'Phew. They don't get closer than that!' gasped a relieved Doorkins. 'I have to say,

Corporal Steadfast, you're a bona-fide hero.'

'All in a day's work, SIR!' She snapped a quick salute at Doorkins.

'Team huddle?' suggested Weasel.

All the animals squeezed in.

'It appears that von Fluff is in a seriously bad mood. If we can get her prize pumpkin to the Best in Show competition, it's bound to win and we might just turn her grump around!'

'But … what about *my* pumpkin?' groaned Doorkins.

'Sorry, old chum,' said Weasel. 'You might just have to take one on the chin for the United Woodlands this time.'

NAARAAAAARH

'Ah, you're right of course, Weasel,' sighed the deflated dormouse.

'That's the spirit, my friend.' Weasel patted his buddy on the back. 'You guys get this great orange beast to the fair, and we'll deal with those pesky scheming foxes!'

Steadfast, being the brave stag beetle she was, volunteered to assist Weasel and Mole in their dangerous pursuit of the fiendish foxes. To everybody's surprise, she opened a pair of wings and took to the air.

'We female stag beetles don't use these much.' She hovered, pointing to her fluttering

wings. 'But now is as good a time as any!'

Is there no end to her amazing abilities? thought Weasel, as they

bolted off towards Farmer Garrett's field.

Doorkins and the fox twins, now more determined than ever to do their bit, set off rolling the giant pumpkin towards the Big Bash. Doorkins crossed his paws for good luck – they were certainly going to need some!

CHAPTER 19

Farmer Garrett's field was just beyond the borders of the United Woodlands. This area was strictly off limits to ordinary Woodlands citizens for a number of reasons – such as spiky barbed wire, sparky electric fences, giant squelchy cowpats and huge, clumsy farm animals.

But for the WI6 spies it was no problem – they were used to missions in dangerous and unfamiliar territory.

As they crept towards the field's hedge, they could hear frantic activity on the other side. Squeezing through a small gap in the hawthorn bushes, carefully avoiding the prickles, the three spies peered out from behind a rusty water trough.

VRUUUMM
VRUUUMM

Foxes scampered around two monstrous motorised sheepdogs, preparing them for action. Weasel had to admit, they'd made a pretty good job of disguising the FFG trucks as border collies. It had certainly convinced the sheep – the flock cowered in the far corner of Garrett's field, trembling with fear.

Von Fluff barked a command at her fox minions and they all piled in the trucks and started to rev their engines.

Thinking quickly, Steadfast grabbed a long piece of blue twine tied to a leg of the heavy water trough, then dashed out behind the nearest truck and knotted it round the bumper. Weasel tied the other end to the second vehicle and dashed back to hide – just in time!

'CHARGE!' howled von Fluff.

Ginger, who was one of the drivers, pushed the truck's accelerator pedal flat to the floor. But the back wheels just spun round and round.

'COME ON, GET A MOVE ON!' von Fluff screeched. 'It's just a bit of sticky mud!'

As the wheels turned faster and faster, muck began to kick up and shower over our unfortunate heroes.

'YUCK, that wasn't the plan!' said Weasel, scooping gloopy mud from his eyes. As he looked up, the trucks lurched forward, tipping the brimming water trough right over the three companions … *SPLOSH!*

Hmmm! A rather sheepy bouquet, thought Weasel, as he snorted greenish water out of his snout. With a high-pitched *VROOM*, the trucks sped off with the large, empty trough in tow.

The sheep did as sheep tend to do, and bolted in the opposite direction from the one the foxes wanted them to go in.

Von Fluff fumed, 'GET THESE DAFT CREATURES MOVING THE RIGHT WAY – OR ELSE!'

VRUMMMM, VRUMMMM … BAAAAAH, BAAAAAAAH … The din was loud

enough to wake a family of hibernating badgers.

'WEASEL, the gate!' cried Mole above the racket.

Weasel snapped his eyes towards the other end of the field. A couple of ne'er-do-well foxes were frantically trying to open the steel gate – the one that led straight to the Autumn Big Bash.

'SUFFERING SCALLYWAGS, let's get over there sharpish!' Weasel yelled, already bounding across the lumpy grass, his keen eyes fixed on the foxes.

'HEY! Paws off that gate, you creeps!' Weasel bellowed, closing in on them.

'Yeah, you and whose army?' snarled a particularly unpleasant-looking fox, lifting a splurge gun directly at Weasel.

KER-SPLAT, KER-SPLAT, KER-SPLAT!

it went.

But Agent Weasel wasn't called a super-spy for nothing!

He dodged the speeding missiles with a massive leap and rotating flip.

His head swam.

He began to see red.

It could be only one thing: the Weasel War Dance was kicking in. As you now know, when a weasel is threatened it can switch into a trance-like state, displaying unbelievable acrobatic feats that can hypnotise and stun its enemies.

The two foxes gazed in amazement as Weasel bounced and spun towards them. But under the War Dance spell, he had failed to notice a large, dry cowpat right in his path. Weasel's paw caught the edge …

'YEEEOOW!' He went flying towards the electric fence, bouncing off one of the plastic poles and forcing the electric wire on to the gate.

BUUUZZZZZT! it went, sending a charge through the metal – and the foxes. They jolted with shock and dropped into a sparky heap on the grass below.

'UUUUUGH!' they groaned, their fur stuck up like dried teasel pods.

'Quick thinking, Agent Weasel!' said Mole as she dashed up.

Weasel's ears were still ringing from his War Dance and he wasn't sure whether he was coming or going.

'Yes, I had it planned all along,' he gasped, giving a guilty look towards the dried cowpat.

On the other side of the field, the flock of sheep was doing a marvellous job. They had von Fluff's drivers zigzagging all over the shop, and the FFG boss looked ready to explode with frustration.

'RIGHT, we'll flatten this fair ourselves! We'll do a better job without these pesky sheep!' von Fluff barked. The trucks turned to face the gate.

But there, directly in their path, were the interfering WI6 spies.

'AAAARRGHHH! No more Mister Nice Fox. GET THEM!' von Fluff roared.

Ginger revved her engine to its max, and the trucks rocketed towards the super-agents at tremendous speed. Wheels and mud flew, the water trough bouncing along behind.

The sheep had gone back to business as usual, calmly munching grass at the back of the field. They glanced up briefly as Weasel cried dramatically:

'YOU SHALL NOT PASS!'

It was a line from a favourite movie he had been saving for just such an occasion. The comrades stood defiantly in front of Farmer Garrett's gate as the FFG sheepdog trucks raced towards them at full speed.

CHAPTER 20

Something buzzy landed on Weasel's head. There was Corporal Steadfast, shouting at the top of her beetly voice: 'DON'T BE DAFT – GET THROUGH HERE NOW!'

There was no doubt: they were about to be completely squished. Weasel grabbed Mole and raced between the bars of the gate.

With the foxes nearly on them, the pair dived for the long grass by the gateway. The trucks smashed the gate as they bashed through, missing the comrades by a hair's breadth as they thundered past.

'PHEW, that was as close as a very close thing! But we've failed. The Autumn Big Bash is surely doomed now,' despaired Weasel.

With an almighty *CLAAAAANG*, the trucks jolted to a stop. The water trough had jammed between the gateposts. The fox crew – apart from von Fluff, who had sensibly worn a seat belt – were flung on to the hard dirt track.

'WELL, DON'T JUST LIE THERE, YOU NINCOMPOOPS,' the fox leader shrieked. 'GET AFTER THEM! This is turning out to be the worst despicable plan EVER!' she grumbled, fumbling to undo her seat belt.

Taking advantage of the foxes' disarray, Weasel and his two trusty teammates rushed off to the fair. It seemed completely deserted. Wonderful smells hit them from all sides as they dashed past the grub stalls: candy

moss, sugared acorns, sticky apple sauce and Weasel's absolute favourite, worm burgers with all the trimmings. His stomach growled like a crotchety polecat and he realised just how hungry he was.

But more growling and snarling was coming from behind them. The foxes were right on their tails!

Weasel spotted Doorkins by the main show tent, waving them over.

'Ha! My good old dormouse buddy made it!' Weasel, Mole and Steadfast headed straight to the main tent, the foxes in close pursuit.

The whole bunch burst through the main tent flap, then stopped dead in their tracks.

It seemed like the entire population of the

United Woodlands was gawping at them. There were red squirrels, grey squirrels, hedgehogs, badgers, rabbits, mice, stoats, beavers, mallards, newts, beetles, crows, otters, hawks, voles, shrews, hares, dragonflies … and that was to name just a few – all looking extremely disgruntled at the interruption.

The unwelcome visitors squirmed.

'Is there a problem over there?' glowered Principal Pine Marten from the stage.

'No, very sorry, do carry on!' came a small apologetic voice from the back.

'Ahem, right! It's the one you've all been waiting for,' announced PPM. 'The Autumn Big Bash Best in Show competition!'

'OOOOOOOOOO!' said the animals.

PPM ripped open a golden envelope, taking her time of course, building the tension.

'And the winner of this year's Best in Show is …' She paused for dramatic effect, like they did on *Woodland's Got Talent*.

'Oh, do get on with it, PPM – we all know it's Doorkins again!' came a heckle from the crowd.

There was a hubbub at the side of the stage. Doorkins edged across to Principal Pine Marten and whispered in her ear. PPM frowned, then nodded, as Doorkins explained everything. It took a little while.

'OH, COME ON!' someone called.

'Yes, well, it appears we have a … erm … last-minute entry!' PPM declared. There was a murmur from the audience.

With a sharp crack, Viv and Vic rolled von Fluff's incredible pumpkin on to the stage, right next to the other prize vegetables. It dwarfed the bloomin' lot of them.

Everybody gasped.

'This changes everything!' said the astonished United Woodlands leader. 'Ahem, well, let's try that again, shall we? And the winner is …' She paused again.

'GET ON WITH IT!' called the annoying heckler.

Principal Pine Marten scowled.

'The winner is … Madam Vixen von Powder-Puff!'

There was absolute silence and a few puzzled looks.

Doorkins beckoned PPM over and whispered in her ear.

'Ah, I see,' she blurted. 'Third time lucky, then. And the winner is … MADAM VIXEN VON FLUFF!'

Well, the foxes went wild, cheering and whooping. They hoisted a stunned von Fluff on to their shoulders and trampled over a few animals to carry her towards the stage.

Principal Pine Marten handed her the famous Best in Show trophy, the Acorn Cup (which of course had Doorkins's name etched all over it).

'We'll have that scraped off when we get back to the den,' von Fluff muttered to Ginger.

'Well, I am truly lost for words,' announced von Fluff to the crowds. But then she managed to find some. 'I came here today to flatten this fair and everyone in it!'

All the animals gasped in shock.

'But as from this moment, I am officially in a good mood. So all fiendish foxiness is off – for now!'

'ERM … HOORAY FOR THE FOXES?' cheered the crowd.

'Phew!' said Weasel, putting an arm around his dormouse friend. 'You certainly saved us there, old chum. Don't worry about the Acorn Cup – there's always next year!'

'I've sort of gone off pumpkins,' Doorkins sighed. 'Time for a change, I think – maybe *cakes*?'

'NOW YOU'RE TALKING!' said Vic, almost knocking the dormouse off his feet with a well-meaning slap to the back.

*

Later, back at Hedgequarters …

'Congratulations, Agent Weasel, on another … er … successful mission?' H said, perching on the corner of her head-honcho desk. 'Not the way I would have seen it going – and definitely NOT by the book! But a good effort.'

'I couldn't have done it without my trusty team,' said Weasel, now reunited with Muriel Moth, who sat on his head fluttering her wings excitedly. 'Doorkins, Steadfast, Mole and Muriel are the best team any agent could hope for.'

'Talking about your team, I'd like to thank those fox-twin double agents,' said H. 'What happened to them?'

'Ah, yes, Viv and Vic,' replied Weasel. 'They've just gone to the WI6 canteen for some well-deserved pudding.'

'Oh, what a shame. That *is* bad luck,' sighed H.

'Why?' asked Weasel.

'The canteen shuts at five o'clock, and Chef Flourplop closes on the dot. It's five minutes past five.'

'WEEEEEEEEEEEASEL! WHERE'S MY *PUDDING*?' a frustrated cry echoed from the floor below.

Weasel, Doorkins, Steadfast and Mole glanced nervously at each other.

'Er … back to Flaky-Bark Cottage for some tea and biscuits – NOW?' suggested Weasel.

And they all barged out of WI6, as quickly as their legs could carry them.

PUDDINGGGGGGGG

NICK EAST is the illustrator of the bestselling
Toto the Ninja Cat as well as the *Goodnight Digger* and
Knock Knock series. He worked for many years as a
museum designer but has always been a storyteller, whether
as a child, filling sketchbooks with quirky characters, or as
a designer displaying a collection of ancient artefacts.
He lives near York with his wife and two children and,
when not writing or drawing, he is out roaming the
countryside with a rucksack on his back.

NICK SAYS:

*Much love to my incredibly supportive family, especially
dear Lou, Finn and Tilly – you are the absolute best!
Heartfelt thanks to Heather Richards, a truly wonderful
and caring agent. A big bear-like hug to my studio buddies
Jonty, Ros, Alfie and Basil. And sincerest gratitude to the
amazing team at Hachette. Particularly the awesome
Rachel Wade and Alison Padley.*

*And last but not least: love to the beautiful Yorkshire
Wolds, my inspiration and sanctuary.*

LOOK OUT FOR AGENT WEASEL AND THE ABOMINABLE DR SNOW